MODERN TRACTORS

MODERN TRACTORS

A Photographic Collection

STEPHEN RICHMOND AND JONATHAN WHITLAM

FARMING PRESS

AUTHORS' NOTE

All the horsepower ratings given in this book are approximate and should be used as a rough guide only. They are, where possible, those stated by the manufacturer's own sales leaflets and publicity material but, as with other details such as transmission systems, optional equipment etc, the figures given may vary from model to model as changes are constantly made to machine specifications. Where equipment is stated in the text as being fitted to a particular tractor, this should again be used only as a guide, as this also varies model to model.

Frontispiece

One of many electronic packed tractors produced by the Italian SLH company is this Lamborghini 165 that is emerging from the dense smoke of a burning bale that somehow got left behind!

Front cover

A John Deere 7800 ploughing after the 1995 harvest with a French built Grégoire Besson six furrow plough.

Back cover

Top: Ford's biggest TW, the TW35, is breaking up tramlines with a three leg Flat-Lift subsoiler.

Bottom: This Massey Ferguson 3080 waits for a well earned clean on a sunny winter's day in January 1995 after finishing carting sugar beet.

First published 1996

Copyright © Stephen Richmond and Jonathan Whitlam 1996

ISBN 0 85236 348 6

A catalogue record for this book is available from the British Library

Published by Farming Press
Miller Freeman Professional Ltd
Wharfedale Road, Ipswich IP1 4LG, United Kingdom

Distributed in North America by Diamond Farm Enterprises Box 537, Alexandria Bay, NY 13607, USA

Cover design and book layout by Hannah Berridge Typeset by Winsor Clarke Typesetting Printed and bound in Great Britain by The Bath Press, Bath

PREFACE

Powerful, high performance engines; electronically controlled transmissions; multiple computer systems and a precisely regulated operator environment: that is the modern agricultural tractor. In this book we have delved into our combined collection of nearly ten thousand photographs to bring together some of the best known, and some of the not so well known, tractor models of the last thirty years or so.

In this period tractors have changed greatly, especially in the areas of driver comfort, improved engine design and the electronic revolution. Hopefully this collection of photographs shows this quite graphically, from the two wheel drive, 45hp Massey Ferguson 135 with a simple metal cab to the JCB Fastrac 1115 with its 115hp and sprung suspension system.

This is by no means intended to be a complete history of the tractor, as it is based only on the tractors and models that we have ourselves encountered and it is inevitable that several manufacturers and their products are not included. We have, however, tried to include as many different makers as possible, while purposely concentrating on the biggest builders as these are the companies that are usually at the forefront of design and technology and set the trends which others follow.

As the title says, the subject of this book is modern tractors and we make no apology for including more models from the past ten years or so than earlier ones, as these are the tractors that are currently virtually ignored in most books available today. It seems that anything that cannot be labelled as 'vintage', i.e. before 1960, is not worth writing about.

We have tried to keep the text to a minimum and let the photographs themselves tell the story, but we have included information such as the tractors' engine power (rated as DIN horsepower as stated by the manufacturer), number of cylinders and, where possible, the number of gear ratios available, so that comparisons can be made between the various models through the years and between some of the other models that appeared at the same time and in the same range as the example depicted.

All the technical information is, as far as we can tell, correct, most of the data being taken from manufacturers' sales leaflets dealing with the actual models concerned.

All the photographs are from our own collection and have never before been published. They show various versions of the modern tractor on display at shows and special events but mostly in their natural environment, either parked at a farm or out working in the fields.

STEPHEN RICHMOND
JONATHAN WHITLAM

INTRODUCTION

▲ *The first Fordson Model F tractors came to Britain in 1917 from America and were the first commercially successful tractors of what is now considered the 'modern' shape. Shown above is the later Model N type, which was introduced in 1929 and built in a new factory in Cork, Ireland. It was powered by a 27.3hp four cylinder petrol/paraffin engine and became probably the most successful tractor model of all time, remaining in production until 1945.*

By the 1960s the diesel powered tractor had virtually replaced all the other forms of motive power on the farm. All the major manufacturers offered a larger range of tractor models than previously, in many cases sold and built on a global scale. The majority of tractors were of two wheel drive, with four wheels at each corner, but some were of tracklayer layout, while quite a number of specialist builders were busy converting some of the leading maker's wheeled models into crawler or four wheel drive format.

The 1970s saw more complex machines arriving along with some of the first major models to be specified with four wheel drive fitted in the factory. But the most important change in this decade was the arrival of the safety cab which had to be fitted to new agricultural tractors and built to an approved and tested design. This led to the start of the luxury cab where the driver could control the temperature and quality of the air in his sealed environment as well as enjoy the benefit of a stereo system.

As the operator's lot improved it was but a short step to the automation of many of his repetitive tasks, and by the middle of the 1980s the first electronic controls had started to appear. These soon blossomed into an array of high-tech electronic engine, transmission and hydraulic controls as well as automatic monitoring of all the tractor's main functions.

With the beginning of the 1990s the tractor's shape itself started to change. The square lines of the previous decades models began to give way to curved, streamlined and all together more aerodynamically designed body work. With this new trend items such as exhaust stacks and air cleaner intake bowls had to forfeit their traditional place on top of the bonnet and found themselves either placed alongside the cab or hidden away under the tinwork. Next the bonnet itself became shorter and narrower and in several models developed a conspicuous droop.

While all this was happening to the wheeled tractors, the crawler or tracklaying tractors remained much the same as they had always been, lumbering around slowly on steel tracks. However, by the 1990s things had changed and they followed their wheeled cousins, with rubber tracks in place of steel, along with computerised controls and even streamlined styling.

▲ *The Model N appeared with bright orange paintwork in 1937, by which time it was made in Dagenham. This rear view shows the simple implement hitch arrangement, dashboard mounted toolbox, pan seat and the single gear lever. No flashing lights and microcomputers here!*

◄ *The American Caterpillar firm was an early user of diesel engines for its range of steel tracked crawlers. This D2 dating from 1938 is powered by a 31hp four cylinder diesel unit. Full-scale use of diesel power in wheeled tractors did not really take off until the late 1940s.*

The 24hp Ferguson TE20 tractor was introduced in 1946 and became extremely popular all over the world. It was fitted with Irish inventor Harry Ferguson's hydraulic three point linkage and draught control system. Virtually every tractor made today is equipped with a modern version of this ingenious system.

Average tractor horsepower increased from about 20hp in the 1940s to around about 100hp in 1996, and it shows no signs of decreasing. Six cylinder engines are now almost universally employed at over 100hp and all are diesel, most being able to run on bio-diesel as well. The latest trend is in speed, with some special tractors being equipped with full air suspension and braking systems to cope with their extra swiftness. Others are built to a design allowing for the fitting of implements at the front, rear and in the middle as well as sprayer tanks and hoppers. The latest version of this idea features a centrally mounted cab and engine to maximise carrying capacity.

◄ *By the 1950s the first weather cabs had appeared and provided the driver with some protection from the elements, if not improving his all-round vision! This is the Fordson New Major which was launched in 1951 and was powered by a 40hp four cylinder engine driving through a six forward and two reverse gearbox. Petrol and tractor vapourising oil driven models were available but the diesel version was by far the most popular.*

◄ *The tractor of the next century? Concept machines have been around for quite some time but in recent years they have become more and more sophisticated and powerful. The most advanced so far is probably the Claas Xerion with its movable cab design; other machines, such as this huge 320hp Vredo VT 3206 unit, are also available. This large tractor is fitted with a Claas cab and has implement mounting points both in front of and behind the cab as well as at the rear of its chassis. Here it is shown with a front mounted forager and a slurry tanker with injector attached to its rear platform.*

Despite all these innovations, the main features of tractor design still remain the same: four wheels (larger at the rear than at the front), forward mounted engine in front of a rear positioned cab and a rear mounted hitch and three point linkage. This looks to be the most popular combination for some years to come, as it is without a doubt the most versatile and a universally accepted standard. The only threat to this in the future may be the growth of multipurpose machines such as the new Claas Xerion which is a high-horsepower machine that can be used with a range of wraparound equipment such as forage and sugar beet harvesters, combination drills, etc. These types of 'tractor', however, are expensive and even if they do displace the normal tractor from the bigger jobs, the traditional machine will still be needed for carting crops from the fields and various other everyday duties.

As can be seen from the following photographs, tractors do not all necessarily remain in the same condition as when they left the factory. Items such as front linkages and power take off shafts are often added; dual wheels fitted to the rear, or sometimes all wheels; turbochargers may be added to increase the engine's power output, and large flotation tyres are often fitted in place of the normal wheels to reduce soil compaction. Plus of course the up-to-date tractor driver may also add a CB radio and aerial, a flashing hazard beacon or two and even the odd sticker!

Today a vast range of tractors are available throughout the world, from small horsepower horticultural and vineyard tractors to massive 500hp articulated machines. In some parts of the world they work non-stop twenty-four hours a day for several months; in others they work in water up to their bonnets, in dusty deserts or in freezing wastes. Here in Britain, they can be seen daily performing all sorts of different tasks and, in the following pages, you will encounter some of them. We certainly feel that without the modern tractor the countryside would be a much less colourful and interesting place.

▲ *1964 saw the launch of Massey Ferguson's DX Series tractors, the smallest of which was the 45hp 135 with its three cylinder Perkins diesel engine and a choice of three gearbox options, including the twelve forward and two reverse Multi-Power transmission fitted to the example shown above. Other models in the range included the 58hp 165 and the 66hp 175.*

The Ford 4000 first appeared in 1964 as the 56hp three ▶  cylinder 4000 Major and was part of the all-new 6X range manufactured in Ford's new factory in Basildon, Essex. In 1968 the entire range received a face-lift and became the 6Y Series, the 4000 being uprated to 62hp, an example of which is shown here with a Bomford Super Trim hedgecutter.

Four wheel drive was not fitted to any of the tractors made ▶  by the major manufacturers until about the late 1970s, thereby leaving a gap in the market for small tractor makers and conversion specialists. Such a company was Muir-Hill, who made their first tractor in 1966 based on Ford components. The 101 was powered by a 108hp six cylinder Ford 2704E industrial engine driving four equal size wheels. The Muir-Hill 121, shown here, was introduced in 1972 and became the successor to the original 101 model in the Gloucester based firm's tractor line-up. It was powered by a 120hp Ford engine and featured several other improvements including a new cab.

▲ *The David Brown 885 formed part of this Yorkshire based firm's tractor range from 1965, and this one is shown drilling sugar beet with a Stanhay six* *row precision drill. A simple safety frame is the driver's only protection on this cold March afternoon in, not 1966, but 1996!*

▲ *This 66hp 175 is shown with a Wilder Twin Chop forage harvester and a type of weather cab that cropped up on several different makes of tractor, such as John Deere, County and Roadless, during the late 1960s and early '70s.*

14

The Leyland tractor first appeared in 1971 and by ▶
1978 the Synchro range was being offered, along with the
company's own synchromesh gearbox and the option of
factory fitted four wheel drive. This 472, seen climbing a
silage clamp, was powered by a 72hp four cylinder engine.

◀ A close-up of the British Leyland badge as fitted to the front
of a smaller three cylinder 45hp 245 tractor dating from
pre-Synchro days, although this particular model was also
available with the synchromesh option from 1978. By 1980 the
range was again updated with new model designations, cabs
and a new gold colour scheme.

▲ *Built at Doncaster, the International Harvester 454 produced 52hp from its three cylinder International engine. This one is shown as it starts to pull out the rain gun of an Irrifrance Javelin drum irrigator into a crop of potatoes.*

▲ *1972 saw the takeover of the British David Brown tractor business by the giant American oil company Tenneco, based in Houston, Texas. As Tenneco were already owners of the J.I. Case tractor and farm machinery company, it was perhaps inevitable that after the two companies were merged, the Case name would later appear alongside that of David Brown on tractors such as this 1210 model of around 70hp.*

◀ When the 6Y Series of Ford tractors were introduced in 1975, the 68hp 5600 became the replacement for the old 5000 model. It was the smallest tractor in the range to be fitted with the optional Dual Power transmission as well as also being available with the Load Monitor load sensing hydraulic system. This 5600 is equipped with the new safety Q cab and is engaged in carting hay bales.

The Doncaster built International 784, here ▶ drilling with a Nordsten drill, is powered by an 80hp four cylinder engine. The standard transmission gives eight forward and four reverse gears; this could be doubled by the fitting of the company's optional Torque Amplifier system.

▲ *The Ford 7700 formed part of the 700 Series range launched in 1976. This was made up of four tractor models ranging from the 78hp 6700 up to the six cylinder 153hp 9700. The latter and the 128hp six cylinder 8700 were the first Ford tractors available in the United Kingdom with factory fitted four wheel drive. As can be seen from this picture of a 97hp four cylinder 7700 carting sugar beet, the 700 Series tractors were built with a longer wheelbase and taller bonnet than the smaller 7A range.*

◀ 1976 was also the year that Massey Ferguson introduced its 500 Series tractors of which the 60hp four cylinder 575, available in either two or four wheel drive and with a new cab, formed a part. The example shown is drilling wheat with a Farmhand drill.

The John Deere 4240S formed part of the large ▶ American firm's 40 Series range and featured a 16 speed Quad-Range gearbox as well as the top-of-the-range SG2 cab. Power comes from a 132hp six cylinder Deere engine.

▲ *For many years Fiat has been one of the largest tractor makers in Europe, but the company has never attained the same level of success in Britain as on the Continent. This 68hp Fiat 680 was equipped with a 12 speed gearbox and clearly shows, despite its venerable age, the bright orange colour scheme of this Italian tractor range.*

▲ *Built in Massey Ferguson's Coventry plant the 200 Series was launched in 1976. This 60hp 265, with the option of either 8 or 12 forward gears, is shown turning on the headland of a field with a three furrow Ransomes plough.*

▲ *Sugar beet drilling with an 82hp four cylinder Lamborghini R854 that is also fitted with an 'A' frame front hitch. An Italian company, Lamborghini is a part of the large Same-Lamborghini-Hürlimann organisation.*

◄ *Taken as the sun was setting, this picture shows the 100hp John Deere 3140 which was fitted with the 16 speed Power-Synchron gearbox and hydrostatic steering.*

The County 7600-FOUR, was based on the 97hp Ford 7600 but ▶ *featured County's powered front axle. When the new Series 10 tractors were introduced in 1981 County continued with the FOUR tractors, based mostly on the 6610 and 7610. However Ford were now offering their own four wheel drive system and County soon reverted to making only equal size wheel conversions, a product for which the company is probably best known.*

▲ *A 67hp David Brown 1390 waits on the headland of a potato field along with a rear mounted haulm pulveriser. The 90 Series machines were the last tractors to carry the David Brown name and were in production from 1979 until their replacement by the similar looking Case 94 Series in 1984.*

▲ *Some of the huge 200hp plus articulated tractors have made their way from the plains of North America to the smaller scale fields of Britain. One that has done so is this John Deere 8440 that dates from the early 1980s. It is shown* *complete with all round dual wheels which help this huge machine to gain even more traction for such jobs as mole draining and cultivation.*

▲ *The new Series 10 Ford tractor range, launched in 1981, brought a whole new line-up of models on the market. This 82hp four cylinder 6610 is fitted with the top-of-the-range Q cab; two* *other new cab options were also available. The smallest tractor in the Series 10 range was the 41hp 2910 while the largest was the 110hp 8210.*

27

▲ *A 92hp Lamborghini 955DT makes its way across a sugar beet field with a full load in its Richard Western dumper trailer. When new in 1982, this tractor cost around £17,200.*

Despite Leyland's restyle in 1980 it was only a matter of months till ▶ the whole of the company's tractor range was sold to the owners of Track Marshall crawlers. This meant that the old Leyland machines were re-badged Marshall but remained basically unchanged. Shown here is a 1984 example of the 82hp four cylinder 802. Fitted with the Explorer cab, this model was also available as the four wheel drive 804 and was the largest tractor in the range until the launch of the bigger 904 and 100 Series models. By the mid 1980s the company had ceased making wheeled tractors and was concentrating on its track laying machines, including a new 200hp rubber tracked model.

◀ The Ford TW range of tractors was originally introduced in 1979 and consisted of three models: the TW10, 20 and 30 ranging from 132hp to 186hp. In 1983 the range received a face-lift and an example of these later machines is shown here — a 154hp six cylinder TW25, which was the replacement for the TW20. It is shown together with a large low loader in a drainage contractors yard. Made in Belgium, the TW Series were the largest European built Ford tractors.

▲ *The 600 Series Massey Ferguson tractors were in production until 1986 and replaced the earlier 500 Series machines. Shown here is a 1984 example of the 75hp 690, which was equipped with MF's Multi-Power twelve speed gearbox.*

▲ An 85hp Renault 95-14 is seen here preparing a seedbed with a Maschio power harrow. This tractor is typical of the machines that were being produced by this French company in the early 1980s and is fitted with a 12 speed gearbox, four wheel drive and a rear lift capacity of 4170kg. The 14 Series range of tractors was one of the first to include electronic information displays inside the cab, and the biggest of the lot was the 135hp six cylinder 145-14.

Tractors from the German Fendt company ▶
have always featured novel ideas, such as the
Turbomatic hydraulically operated fluid clutch
and twenty speed transmission that was fitted to
this 145hp six cylinder Fendt Favorit 614 LSA.

◀ *This four wheel drive version of the*
82hp four cylinder Lamborghini
854DT, new in 1985, was one of the
last of its type to be made before the
introduction of a completely new line of
models. Interestingly, as part of the
Same-Lamborghini-Hürlimann group,
this design of tractor was also available
as the red 88hp Same Leopard 90T and
the pale green 82hp Hürlimann H480.

This 88hp Massey Ferguson 698 has been fitted with an Opico ▶ *turbocharger to boost the power from its four cylinder Perkins engine. This was the biggest tractor in the 600 Series range until 1984, when the 95hp six cylinder 699 model was introduced, replacing the smallest 2000 Series tractor, the 2620.*

◀ *All three ranges in the Italian Same-Lamborghini-Hürlimann stable received a face-lift in 1985 with a complete restyle. The Hürlimann range, originally built in Switzerland, was now led by the top-of-the-range 165hp six cylinder and turbocharged H-6170T. The one here, complete with trailer, has just tipped a load of wheat in a barn.*

▲ *The same Hürlimann H-6170T as shown in the previous picture.*

▶ *1985 saw the Ford Series 10 tractors become the improved Force II range. Three cab options were still available including the LP cab shown here on a 61hp three cylinder 4610. The LP (Low Profile) option was most popular with livestock farmers who appreciated the cab's lower height and cost, and who did not mind the lack of a radio!*

◀ *The middle of the range cab was the All Purpose or AP cab, an example of which is shown here fitted to a 98hp four cylinder Ford 7610 that is cultivating stubble with a Bomford Dyna-Drive.*

▲ *The Massey Ferguson 2000 Series tractors were introduced in 1979 and spanned four models from the 95hp 2620 to the flagship 147hp 2720. All were assembled at MF's Beauvais factory in France and featured Perkins six cylinder engines. In 1984 the 2005 Series was launched replacing the earlier range and* *including over thirty improvements. The 130hp 2680 now became the 2685 and this version, shown after completing a day's work with a JF forage harvester, was equipped with Massey Ferguson's optional electronically controlled hydraulic three point linkage, as well as a 16 speed Speedshift transmission.*

▲ *A contractor's 93hp six cylinder John Deere 3050, equipped with the company's Power-synchron transmission, rushes up the headland of a field with a full trailer of sugar beet.*

▲ *Case International was formed in 1985 by the merger of J. I. Case and International Harvester, and as a result the Case 94 Series tractors were now available in a new dark red livery. Still built in the old David Brown factory in Yorkshire, the complete range consisted of the 48hp 1194 up to the 108hp 1694,* *with four larger machines being imported from America, the largest of which was the 277hp 4894. This 95hp Case International 1594 is shown here working with a gang of Cambridge rolls.*

▲ *The 6 Series range of Lamborghini six cylinder tractors were with us by 1985 and the smallest of the range, the 95hp 956, is shown here baling with a Claas Rollant 44 round baler. It featured the Lamborghini 916.6W engine and a 24 forward by 12 reverse gearbox.*

▲ *This 82hp four cylinder Ford 6610 clearly shows the new Super Q cab that was introduced with the Force II range of tractors in 1985. As Ford's top-of-the-range cab it featured no less than four extra worklights on the front of its roof.*

▼ *The 105hp six cylinder Case International 1056 XL is shown here complete with Maschio power harrow and Accord pneumatic drill combination. The seed hopper is front mounted to help spread the considerable weight of this large piece of tackle.*

▲ *Sister to the 1056 was the slightly smaller 95hp 956 XL, a view inside the cab of which is shown here. Like the 1056, the 956's eight forward and four reverse gears are controlled by two small gear levers which, by the use of a gear splitter, can be increased to a total of 16 X 8.*

▲ *The 98hp six cylinder Ford 7910 first appeared in 1984 but, like the rest of the Series 10 models, it was revamped in 1985 to become part of the Force II range. This example, with a user modified lighting arrangement, looks particularly imposing in two wheel drive form.*

▲ *Fiatagri was formed in 1984 with the merger of Italian tractor maker Fiat, combine maker Laverda and the American Hesston machinery company. This 80hp 80-90 DT is a good example of the Fiat tractor range in the latter half of the 1980s, the orange colour scheme of the earlier 80 Series machines having been replaced by the new terracotta paint of the 90 Series tractors.*

▲ *Complete with Reekie potato planter this John Deere 2850 is powered by a four cylinder 85hp Deere engine and is shown with the SG2 cab unique to John Deere.*

◀ ▲ *With the advent of the Ford Force II range in 1985, the TW Series tractors joined the Series 10 machines in sharing the new Super Q cab. This is the biggest, the 186hp six cylinder turbocharged TW35, seen here at work with a seven furrow Grégoire Besson semi mounted plough. It is equipped with a 16 forward and 8 reverse Dual Power transmission.*

▲ *Another large tractor was the 145hp six cylinder Case International 1455 XL. This was the biggest tractor in the European built Case International range and was made in Germany. It also has the distinction of being the last* *International Harvester style tractor to be produced, surviving well into the 1990s, after the rest of the 85 and 95 Series models had been discontinued.*

In 1986 Massey Ferguson introduced a completely ▶
new design of tractor. The 3000 and 3600 Series
machines spanned a wide range from 71 to 180hp. This
is the 93hp 3070, powered by a Perkins four cylinder
diesel engine, and shown here breaking down ploughed
land with a set of Cousins rollers.

Inside the cab of the 3070 showing the dashboard ▶
instrumentation. These tractors were trendsetters at the
time of their launch and the first to include electronic
monitoring and control functions through the use of
Massey Ferguson's Autotronic or optional Datatronic
systems.

▲ *When originally launched the 125hp six cylinder Lamborghini 1306 was the largest in the Italian firm's 6 Series range. It is fitted with a turbocharged version of the 916.6WT engine fitted to the smaller 956, and also shares that tractor's 24 X12 gearbox. Note the large front linkage fitted to this particular example.*

▲ *Replacing the 699 in the new Massey Ferguson range was the 100hp six cylinder 3080, shown here ploughing with a five furrow Lemken plough and furrow press. A choice of two transmissions was available throughout the 3000* *Series range, either 16 X16 or 32 X 32 synchromesh gearboxes with speedshift and a reverse shuttle. All the 3000 Series tractors were made in Beauvais, France.*

The 100hp six cylinder Ford 7810 appeared a couple of ▶ years after the launch of the rest of the Ford Force II range and became the replacement for the 7910. Made in Basildon, the 7810 was destined to become Ford's best-selling tractor, as 100hp six cylinder machines gained in popularity. Working for a contractor on lime spreading duties, the example shown has received a few modifications during its life, such as a new chrome exhaust and resprayed rear mudguards, the latter being originally white.

This Massey Ferguson 3645 is equipped with the Datatronic computer ▶ system and is powered by a 145hp Perkins six cylinder diesel engine. As this is a 1989 example it is possible that it is also fitted with the optional Memotronic computer, that records all the data recorded by the Datatronic sensors and stores it for transferral to a microcomputer back at the farm at a later time.

◀ Another 145hp tractor was the Lamborghini 1506, shown here negotiating a headland turn with an impressive front mounted cultivator press, and with a six metre wide Lely Roterra power harrow on the rear. It featured a six cylinder turbocharged Lamborghini 1106/14T water-oil cooled diesel engine, and the same gearbox as that offered on the 1306. A larger version, the 165hp 1706, was introduced at the same time as the 1506.

▲ *Fiatagri 100hp six cylinder 95-90 at work with a New Holland 650 round baler, baling a crop of hay.*

▲ *1988 saw the first completely new tractors from the Case International stable. The 7100 Magnum Series was made up of four models from 155 to 246hp, the biggest being the first tractor of such power to be built on a rigid chassis instead of the articulated layout that was then the accepted norm. All the Magnums were fitted with 8.3 litre six cylinder turbocharged engines and the new Silent Guardian II cab. Other new features included a single gear lever controlling an eighteen speed full powershift gearbox, electronically controlled hydraulic functions and a side mounted exhaust stack next to the cab. This 182hp 7120 is shown equipped with all-round flotation tyres, making an impressive sight as it hauls a large, similarly equipped slurry tanker along the road.*

◀ *This 110hp six cylinder DX6.05 Commander formed part of the German Deutz-Fahr's tractor range in the late 1980s, and this one is fitted with dual rear wheels and a Kongskilde Germinator cultivator folded up into its transport position.*

◀ *A close-up shot of the front radiator grill of another Deutz-Fahr tractor, this time an 82hp four cylinder DX3.90 from the smaller DX3 Series. The KHD badge represents Deutz-Fahr's parent company: Klöckner-Humboldt-Deutz.*

◄ *Built at the Massey Ferguson tractor plant at Banner Lane in Coventry, the 300 Series range of tractors were originally launched in 1986 and, after an upgrade in 1989, they appeared as shown here by this 80hp four cylinder 390 cutting back the growth in a fieldside ditch with a Bomford hedgecutter.*

A view through the door of the same Massey Ferguson 390 clearly showing the centrally ▶ *positioned gear levers. This is the Low Profile cab that is available as a cheaper option than the taller Hi-line version that has its gear levers positioned to the driver's right and can be specified with a greater number of extra items such as air conditioning. The entire 300 Series range comprise models from the 47hp three cylinder 350, up to the only six cylinder model, the 104hp 399, all powered by Perkins power plants.*

▲ In 1989 Caterpillar, the American firm best known for its large range of construction equipment, ushered in a new era in agricultural tracklayer design with its 285hp Challenger 65 crawler. This machine broke new ground with its rubber tracks which enabled the tractor to use ordinary roads at a speed of up to 18 mph, something that was simply impossible with its predecessors, which all had steel tracks that would have caused considerable damage to road surfaces.

▲ As one of the pioneers of the 'system tractor' concept, the German Fendt company have been producing toolcarrier type tractors since 1953. The front of these tractors is basically a frame from which implements can be slung and hoppers or tanks can be attached; the added advantage of a front linkage makes no less than three implement attaching points possible. This is the 115hp six cylinder F395GT version which, like the other Fendt toolcarriers, features its engine mounted beneath the cab at the rear.

◀ *In 1989 the Ford tractor range received its third face-lift in a decade with the Generation III Series 10 tractors. The new range were fitted with redesigned fuel pumps, cylinder heads, pistons and camshafts, among other improvements. Externally, however, they differed little from the earlier Series 10 except that two new models were introduced: the 80hp four cylinder 6410 and the 90hp 6810, also with four cylinders. In the top picture a 6810 is drilling winter wheat with a Nordsten drill, while in the lower photograph a close-up of the bonnet of another 6810 clearly shows the Generation III logo.*

▲ *The Perkins powered 93hp four cylinder Massey Ferguson 398 was the second biggest tractor in the 300 Series range and is shown fitted with the Low Profile cab, this time with the addition of optional worklights mounted at the front of the roof.*

▲ *This 100hp six cylinder John Deere 3350 typifies the shape of the 1980s Deere tractors with its SG2 cab and tall air filter intake pipe. It was made at John Deere's Mannheim factory in Germany.*

▲ *1989 saw the Ford TW Series tractors undergo their final metamorphosis as they received new model numbers, new colour schemes and the option of a new electronic gearbox. The TW15, 25 and 35 now became the 8630, 8730 and 8830 respectively. The new 18 x 9 full powershift gearbox was controlled by a single lever and included a digital display to inform the driver of which gear had been selected. Although the transmission was significantly more advanced than that fitted to the TW models, the spool valves, three point linkage and pto systems remained unchanged. This is the middle-of-the-range 154hp six cylinder 8730 turning in stubble with a disc plough and following press.*

The 14 Series Renault tractors ▶
disappeared in 1990 to be replaced by
the new 54 Series. This is one of the
smaller models, the 103-54, featuring
an MWM 93hp four cylinder
turbocharged engine, and the TX cab.
These two examples are shown
harvesting grass for silage with a
Mengele forage harvester and silage
trailer.

◀ Fiatagri launched its Winner
Series tractors in 1990, the smallest
being the 100hp F100 followed by
the 110hp F110 and then the
118hp F120, all with six cylinder
engines. 1994 saw the range
restructured with three new models
joining the F100: the 115hp F115,
130hp F130 and the 140hp F140.
The F110 and F120 were
discontinued. This Winner F130 is
shown hauling a set of Parmiter
disc harrows and Simba press with
the 130hp turbocharged Fiat-Iveco
engine driving through a 16 x 16
gearbox.

The new Formula range of Lamborghini tractors consisted of three models from 103 to 135hp. These pictures show two examples of the smallest: the 103hp four cylinder turbocharged 105. The close-up of the tractor bonnet in the bottom picture shows the flamboyant lines and decals that have become a trademark of the Lamborghini machines. In the top photograph a 105 is drilling with a Massey Ferguson 30 drill. Fitted with a 40 x 40 gearbox and capable of a top speed of 25 mph, the 105 could also be specified with the optional Datatrol electronic monitoring system for automatic control of implement depth and height. The 105 was joined by three smaller models in the Grand Prix range, which spanned 70, 80 and 90hp models sharing the same styling and much of the same specification. The other two bigger six cylinder Formula models were built to a larger format.

▲ The JCB Fastrac, as the name suggests, was built with speed in mind. Designed from the wheels up as a fast 'systems tractor', the initial range consisted of two six cylinder models: the 117hp 125 and the bigger 140hp 145 Turbo, shown here. Both tractors were capable of speeds of up to 45 mph on the road as well as able to carry out normal farming jobs, such as ploughing. Unlike conventional tractors they are equipped with air brakes and an air suspension system. There is also space at the rear of the cab, above the rear axle, to accommodate sprayer tanks and seed and fertiliser hoppers.

▲ *The John Deere 55 Series of high horsepower tractors were launched in 1990. This American built range consisted of the 128hp 4055, 144hp 4255, 190hp 4755 and the 228hp 4955, the last of which was the biggest John Deere tractor of over 200hp to be of a non-articulated type. All of these machines featured 7.6 litre six cylinder turbocharged Deere engines and the SG2 cab. The 190hp 4755* is shown here on the road whilst carting sugar beet from a self-propelled harvester. By 1994 only the two biggest tractors in the range were still in production and these were then fitted with an exhaust stack mounted near the side of the cab as in this example.

▼ *This 110hp 120-54 Renault is powered by a six cylinder MWM D226.6 engine and fitted with the TZ cab. Externally the new 54 Series tractors differed little from their six cylinder 14 Series predecessors, with just a redesigned and more curved front grill section. Even this top-of-the-range TZ cab first appeared on the older 14 range. This cab uses a special suspension system consisting of large springs under the cab floor, to protect the driver from shocks produced by riding over rough ground. Inside the cab, the gear levers that operate the tractor's 16 X 16 gearbox and other controls can be clearly seen.* ▶

◀ *The middle model in the Lamborghini Formula range is the 115hp six cylinder 115, seen below ploughing with a Krone four furrow plough. Specification includes a 25 mph transmission (available in either 36 X 36 or 48 X 48 versions), electronic performance monitor, radar sensing and electronic pre-set hand throttle. Inside the cab, which can be specified with air conditioning, the noise level is only 78 dBA, and several functions can be controlled by a touch-pad system mounted on the cab pillar to the right of the driver. This design is also available as part of the Same and Hürlimann tractor ranges.* ▼

▲ *Introduced in 1990, the Case International Maxxum 5100 Series tractors followed the Magnum as the second all-new Case IH design. The range comprised three models from the four cylinder 90hp 5120 up to the six cylinder 110hp 5140. Shown here is the six cylinder 100hp Maxxum 5130, which like the rest of the range, is fitted with a 16 x 16 semi-powershift gearbox that could also be fitted with an extra 8 x 8 creeper option if required. These tractors were among the first within this power group to offer a clutchless shuttle which is operated via a lever on the steering column.*

▲ *The first Russian Belarus tractors appeared in Britain in 1969 and by 1983 six models were being offered, from the 29hp 250 up to the large pivot steer 150 hp 1500. This is a later version of the 1500, the articulated 1507, seen here spreading manure with a Richard Western spreader on a cold winter's morning.*

Before the outbreak of civil unrest in the former Yugoslavia, the IMT tractor company was a major manufacturer in Europe. Once a subsidiary of Massey Ferguson, they continued making their version of the 1960s MF 35 right up into the 1990s. This bigger model, still showing a Massey Ferguson influence, was at the 1991 Royal Norfolk Show.

Silver painted versions of the Renault 54 Series tractors appeared ▶ *in 1991 and were dubbed the Nectra. The 145hp six cylinder 155-54 Nectra shown here is equipped with large flotation tyres to reduce damage to the soil structure whilst it is engaged in spreading sugar beet lime sludge.*

WIDE VEHICLE

▲ Italian tractor maker Landini was once part of the Massey Ferguson company, manufacturing MF tractors in Italy under licence. When the two firms parted company, Landini continued to make use of Perkins engines and the cabs and styling from the now-outdated Massey Ferguson 600 and 2000 Series ranges. The 8880 shown is powered by a Perkins 80hp four cylinder engine, and optional equipment included a choice of six different gearboxes.

◄ 1991 was a big year for Ford tractor operations. Not only was a brand new tractor range launched but the year also saw the acquisition of a large part of the shares of Ford New Holland, of which Ford tractors were now a part, by the Italian Fiatagri organisation. The new tractors were the 40 Series, which replaced the Series 10 models and spanned 75 to 120hp. Shown is the mid-range 95hp four cylinder 7740 SLE, here with a full load of sugar beet in its Richard Western dumper trailer. The 40 Series tractors were all made at Basildon in Essex and were equipped with a wealth of electronic controls for the three point linkage, pto and monitoring systems, as well as a semi-powershift ElectroShift transmission giving 16 X 16 gears, to which could be added a creeper speed option giving up to 24 X 24. The new cab featured a larger glass area and a quieter environment for the driver.

A close-up of the front of the bonnet of another 7740, this ▶ time of SL configuration. The SL version was available on all models except the six cylinder 8240 and 8340 and included a 24 X 24 Dual Power synchromesh gearbox instead of the ElectroShift version. The word 'PowerStar' above the SL is the name given to the new engines designed and built at Basildon for the 40 Series range.

◀▲ *At the time of its introduction, Deutz-Fahr's AgroStar cab was claimed by its German manufacturer to be the quietest on the market with only 75.2dBA noise level at the driver's ear. This 143hp six cylinder Deutz-Fahr DX6.61 models the AgroStar cab in these two pictures, along with a Vaderstad cultivator-drill combination, all-round dual wheels, front linkage with pto and a bucket on top of the exhaust stack!*

77

▲ *Launched at the same time as the Lamborghini Formula tractor range and sharing the same body styling and other components, the Same Antares line-up consists of three models from 100 to 127hp. Like the Lamborghini tractors, the Antares machines can be fitted with the SBA system which automatically engages and disengages four wheel drive and the differential lock. Three choices of transmission are available, either 24 X 12, 36 X 36 or 48 X 48. The flagship of the range, the 127hp six cylinder Antares 130, is seen here with a JF FCT 900 forage harvester.*

▲ *The Caterpillar Challenger 65 rubber tracked crawler was joined in the early 1990s by the more powerful 325hp six cylinder Challenger 75C, shown here ploughing with a Dowdeswell ten furrow plough. Equipped with a full powershift 10 x 2 transmission, the 75C's CAT engine is also electronically controlled. 1994 saw the launch of the biggest Caterpillar crawler yet, the 355hp 85C.*

◀ *French tractor maker Renault added a new six cylinder tractor to its range by 1991, the 175-74, which was the largest tractor in the firm's line-up. It featured a 165hp turbocharged engine and fitted in above the largest 54 Series machine, the 145hp 155-54. This one is used by a contractor and is fitted with oversize wheels.*

This deceptively small looking ▶ *tractor packs 70hp from its turbocharged three cylinder engine and has a top speed of 25 mph. The Lamborghini 700 comes with a 12 X 12 synchro-shuttle transmission or an optional 16 X 16 gearbox is available. It shares its styling with the smaller 60hp 600. A Twin System version is also made which allows the tractor to be driven in reverse with the seat and controls facing in the direction of travel.*

◀▲ *The two biggest models in the Ford 40 Series range were the six cylinder 110hp 8240 and the 120hp 8340. In the latter half of 1993, the 8340's power was increased to 125hp and one such tractor is shown on the facing page ploughing with a five furrow Overum plough. The picture above gives a view from the driving seat of the 8340, clearly showing the slim-line exhaust. The two work lamps fitted to the front of the cab are visible on the bottom left and right hand sides of the photograph.*

◀ ▶ *By the 1990s the largest tractors in the Massey Ferguson range were the 170hp 3670 and 190hp 3690. These two tractors were unique in featuring six cylinder Valmet engines built in Finland, instead of the Perkins units fitted to the rest of the Massey Ferguson range. Pictured is a late version of the 3690 which is fitted with the Dynashift semi-powershift transmission giving 32 X 32 gears as well as the Datatronic electronic monitoring system. It is seen to the left ploughing with a seven furrow Naud articulated plough. The maximum lift capacity of this large tractor's rear linkage is 7800kg.*

Part of the Italian Landini tractor range, the Blizzard 95 ▶ *Excel is powered by a 90hp Perkins four cylinder engine and is equipped with a 24 forward and 12 reverse gearbox. The Blizzard range was one of the first all-new ranges to be launched after Massey Ferguson ceased to be the company's largest shareholder in 1990.*

▲ *John Deere introduced its 6000 and 7000 Series tractors in 1992. The larger 7000 range was initially made up of three models: the 130hp 7600, 150hp 7700 and the 170hp 7800. The flagship 7800 is shown here ploughing with a six furrow Grégoire Besson plough. Fitted with the all-new TechCenter cab, the American built 7000 tractors are equipped with an exhaust stack positioned next to the cab and a full powershift 19 X 7 PowrQuad transmission, controlled by a single lever.*

▲ Introduced in 1992 the Lamborghini 165 Racing features a 165hp turbocharged and intercooled engine and is absolutely bristling with electronics and computer controlled aids. These include an electronically controlled 27 X 27 powershift gearbox, SBA system, electronic three point linkage control and radar monitoring. The 165 was later joined by the 189hp 190 and the 150hp 150 in the Lamborghini Racing range. This 165 is ploughing with a Krone five furrow plough and is fitted with a front linkage.

▲ *Mechanically speaking still an International Harvester 885 from the 1980s, the 82hp four cylinder Case International 895 XL was restyled for the 1990s with a bonnet and cab roof design plus a digital dashboard borrowed from the bigger Maxxum range. The designation Duo used in this tractor's last few years of production came from the fact that it was fitted with two sets of spool valves, two assister rams and a two speed mechanical powershift transmission and sold at a special price of £22,222. This one is harvesting potatoes with a Standen Wuhlmas harvester.*

▲ *Equipped with flotation tyres on all four wheels, this Deutz-Fahr 6.31 with AgroStar cab makes an impressive sight as it works a Rabe power harrow drill combination plus a front mounted Farm Force press.*

▲ Massey Ferguson's Dynashift transmission was available only on 3600 Series tractors until 1993, when it was introduced to the 3100 models and the 3095. In addition the 100hp six cylinder 3080 became the Dynashift equipped 3085, and this one is shown preparing a seedbed with a set of spring tine cultivators while running on large flotation tyres at the rear.

▼ Introduced in November 1992 at the same time as the 7000 Series machines, the 6000 range was initially made up of four models: the 75hp 6100, 84hp 6200, 90hp 6300 and the 100hp 6400; all were equipped with four cylinder Deere engines. They were built to a new full frame design and featured new electronic gearbox and hydraulic systems. Below is the top-of-the-range 6400 hoeing a field of sugar beet with a front mounted twelve row hoe.

▲ Inside John Deere's new TechCenter cab showing the gear selection levers which control the PowrQuad gearbox. Three versions of this transmission are available on the 6000 Series tractors — 16 X 12, 20 X 16 or 24 X 16 — and an optional creeper range gives another 12 speeds in both forward and reverse. This cab belongs to the 6600 shown overleaf.

▲ *By late 1993 John Deere had added two more models to the 6000 Series range, the 110hp 6600 and the 120hp 6800, both powered by six cylinder diesels. As can be seen by this picture of a 6600, collecting wheat from a Claas combine, the two new tractors shared the same styling as the previous 6000 models.*

◀ *The JCB Fastrac range were updated in 1993 with revised styling and three models instead of the previous two. These were the 120hp 125-65, 135hp 135-65 and the 150hp 155-65. This particular 135-65, which like the rest of the range features a Perkins six cylinder engine, was waiting on the headland of an oilseed rape field with a Brian Legg trailer.*

▲ Ploughing with a Rabe four furrow slatted mouldboard plough, this 105hp four cylinder Valmet 6600 forms part of this Finnish maker's range of tractors which include models from 61 to 190hp. It is fitted with a 36 x 36 gearbox.

▲ *The Case International Maxxum range received a face-lift in 1993 with several new features and a new top-of-the-range 125hp model. Here, the 100hp six cylinder Maxxum Plus 5130 is shown baling wheat straw with a John Deere round baler. Note the extra work lights on the top of the cab.*

◄ *In 1993 the Renault 175-74 was replaced by a new flagship model, the 170hp six cylinder turbocharged 180-94. It is fitted with a new Multishift electronic powershift transmission that is built by the Italian SLH group and provides 27 x 27 gears.*

Inside the cab of the Renault 180-94 the movable ► *console that contains the controls for the transmission system can be clearly seen. This console also houses controls for operating four wheel drive, the pto, diff lock and even a computer controlled self-diagnostic system. Another 94 Series tractor appeared later, the 150hp 160-94.*

▲ *A Case International Maxxum Plus 5150 pauses while ploughing. With a six cylinder 125hp engine this is the biggest of the Maxxum range and features slightly different bonnet styling.*

◄ *Another view of a Case International Maxxum 5150, clearly showing its large flotation tyres and an impressive front mounted Dowdeswell furrow press. The plough it was using, which is not visible here, was a five furrow Dowdeswell.*

The Massey Ferguson 399 has a 104hp six cylinder Perkins ▶ diesel engine driving through an 18 X 6 gearbox. Although the Coventry built 300 Series tractors are designed to be a more basic alternative to the mainstream Beauvais ranges, a certain degree of electronic instrumentation is now available on models such as this, which is fitted with the Hiline cab.

▲ *In May 1994 Case International replaced its 95 Series tractors with the new 3200 (52 to 60hp) and 4200 (70 to 90hp) ranges. The 82hp four cylinder 4230 shown here is fitted with the new LP (Low Profile)* cab *that was introduced along with the new tractors and includes a window in the roof to aid visibility when being used with a front loader.*

◀▲ *The German Mercedes-Benz vehicle maker is well known for its luxury cars and range of vans and trucks; they have also been active in the field of agricultural tractors. The first of the firm's Unimog vehicles appeared just after the Second World War and were later joined by a range of equal size wheel tractors. Tractor production stopped in the early 1990s, however, in favour of the more versatile Unimog, which is a cross between a four wheel drive truck and a tractor. Today three models make up the main agricultural range, although others are also available. Shown here is the biggest, the 214hp U2100, which,*

like the others, is fitted with a six cylinder diesel engine and 16 x 16 gearbox, and it is pictured with a Dowdeswell power harrow. As the Unimog is based on a truck type chassis, the cab is mounted towards the front of the vehicle, leaving room on the rear for such items as spray tanks, fertiliser and seed hoppers and lime spreaders. The faster road speed that can be reached by the Unimog puts it, along with the JCB Fastrac and the Fendt Xylon, in a group of machines that have been given the title of 'system tractors'.

▲ *Another tractor from the Case International 4200 Series is the 90hp four cylinder 4240. This is a 1996 example which features more power, now 92hp, side engine panels and a new Case IH logo. It is still fitted with the XL cab and 16 X 8 gearbox from the original model and is shown powering a Claas Jaguar forage harvester.*

◀ *The sloping bonnet concept, or droop-nosed as it is often called, was first introduced by Deutz-Fahr in 1990 on the AgroXtra range of tractors, built in Cologne, Germany. The five initial models were 80 to 113hp. Three later models in 1993 — two larger, 115 and 125hp, and one slightly smaller, 107hp — all of which were fitted with the AgroStar cab, brought the number of sloping bonnet Deutz tractors up to eight models. The sloping bonnet design helps to improve forward visibility, which is especially useful for front loader and front linkage work. Several other tractor manufacturers have followed Deutz-Fahr's lead and produced droop-nosed tractors, such as Massey Ferguson with its 3065 HV, Case International, Landini and Steyr. This 107hp 6.08 Deutz-Fahr is shown at the Suffolk Show in 1995, the same year in which the German company was taken over by the Italian SLH group which later became known as Same-Deutz-Fahr.*

◀▶ *The Massey Ferguson 3120 was launched in 1993 and featured a Perkins Quadram 120hp six cylinder engine. This particular example was on demonstration at the time it was photographed and was ploughing with a Dowdeswell four furrow plough. The 3120 replaced the 115hp 3115.*

Two models made up the original MF range which ▶ fitted in the gap between the 110hp 3095 and the 135hp 3635. These were the 115hp six cylinder 3115 and the 126hp 3125. An example of the latter is seen here ploughing with a five furrow Naud plough. This tractor is also fitted with Dynashift, Datatronic and a front linkage.

The biggest tractor in the Fiatagri Winner range is shown ▶
here with a Lely Roterra power harrow. Powered by a 140hp
six cylinder Fiat-Iveco engine, the F140 is also equipped with
a 12 X 12 transmission that is boosted by a creeper range to 24
X 12. Another feature of the Winner tractors is the graphic
display on the dashboard which illuminates if its sensors detect
a fault.

Valmet from Finland are unique among tractor ▶
manufacturers in offering the tractor buyer a choice of colour
schemes. This 85hp four cylinder 6300 is shown wearing a
blue livery and is in two wheel drive form.

▲ Following the success of the bigger Challenger crawlers, the American Caterpillar organisation introduced two smaller models in 1994. The 205hp Challenger 35 and the 235hp 45 are built to a different design than their bigger cousins, and share styling, cab and gearbox similar to that used on the New Holland Ford 70/Fiatagri G Series tractors introduced in the same year. In fact, the crawlers are built in the same factory as these tractors, in the Versatile plant in Winnipeg, Canada. The CAT six cylinder engine drives through a 16 X 9 Funk transmission controlled by a single lever and the Challenger 35 above is shown with a six metre wide Dowdeswell power harrow. In 1996 a larger 275hp Caterpillar appeared, designated the Challenger 55.

◀▲*This huge 375hp Case International 9280 makes easy work of pulling a twelve furrow plough. It is built by Steiger, who have been making large four wheel drive tractors in Minnesota since 1957 and for many years produced the FW Series for Ford. This came to an end, however, when Steiger was acquired by Case International in 1986. The 9280 gets its substantial power from a six cylinder turbocharged Cummins diesel engine and is equipped with a full powershift transmission. Quite a surprising number of these and other large articulated tractors are at work in Britain today, especially in East Anglia, although their natural home is on the large wheat plains of North America.*

Landini offer two droop-nosed tractors in their range, the 71hp 7880 ▶ *Viewmaster and the 80hp 8880 shown here. It is fitted with a 24 X 12 Powerflow transmission.*

◀▶ *Introduced in late 1993, the Massey Ferguson 3075 was the smallest tractor to feature the Dynashift powershift transmission and proved to be the last new model to be introduced in the 3000, 3100 and 3600 ranges. It is powered by a four cylinder 98hp turbocharged Perkins engine and the view into the cab shows the main controls and the air suspension seat. This example is pictured to the right parked in a farmyard with a home-made cultivator drill made from a Nordsten drill and a set of spring tine cultivators. A front mounted Flexi-coil press completes the outfit.*

▲ *The beginning of 1994 saw the birth of the Ford 70 Series from New Holland Ford. These four models, spanning 170 to 240hp, replaced the 8630, 8730 and 8830 and featured several new features including a bigger 18 X 9 version of the 30 Series transmission (36 X 18 with the addition of an optional creeper speed range), a movable console housing the single gear lever and other controls. The transmission becomes completely automatic in tenth gear, and these tractors also come with the option of the new Super steer front axle which allows a 65 degree turning angle, made possible by a pivoting front axle, moving weights and frame. With no less than three computers looking after the machine's array of electronics, these tractors are made in the Versatile plant in Winnipeg, Canada and have PowerStar engines built in Basildon, Essex. This is the 240hp six cylinder turbocharged and intercooled 8970, together with a seven furrow Dowdeswell plough.*

112

◄ *By 1994 the Fendt 800 Series had replaced the old 600 Series machines. This 190hp 818 Favorit is shown in reverse drive form and with a Claas Corto 8100F hydraulic folding mower (top) and (below) ploughing with a five furrow plough. The Fendt Favorit 800 range consists of four models: the 816 (165hp), 818 (190hp), 822 (210hp) and the 824 (230hp). All were fitted with six cylinder MAN engines, a 50 kph 44 x 44 gearbox and a rear linkage lift capacity of 9180kg. The 800 Series are also well endowed with electronic gadgetry for controlling and monitoring all major tractor functions.*

▲ ▶Launched in 1994 the new JCB Fastrac 185-65 brought the Fastrac into the 170hp power band. Powered by a Cummins six cylinder 170hp turbocharged and intercooled engine, the new machine carried all the features of the 150, 135 and 120hp models, except of course for the Perkins 1000 Series engine. The transmission provides 36 X 12 gears and is available in either 40 or 45 mph format.

▲ *Autumn 1994 saw the introduction of the John Deere 8000 Series. New from the ground up, these machines replaced what was left of the old 55 Series tractors. Made up of four models — the 8100 (185hp), 8200 (210hp), 8300 (230hp) and the 8400 (260hp) — the 8000 machines feature a Deere six cylinder turbocharged and intercooled engine mounted with most of its weight forwards, over the front axle, a feature made easier by the tractor's full-frame chassis design. This is the 210hp 8200. Note the generous number of worklamps and the huge front radiator grill.*

▲ *The Landini Legend Series of six cylinder tractors is made up of three models from 110 to 138hp. This is the 127hp Perkins powered Legend 130 which, like the other two models, is fitted with a 36 X 36 gearbox.*

▲ *The 115hp six cylinder Fendt Farmer 311 makes up part of this German firm's comprehensive tractor range fitting in between the 200 and 500 Series models. This example is shown putting two swaths of mown grass into one large enough for a huge Claas Jaguar self propelled forager to gobble up efficiently. It is using a Claas Liner 780 tedder.*

▲ *The beginning of 1994 saw the first all-new tractors appear from the now combined forces of Ford and Fiatagri. While the Ford tractors were known as the 70 Series (see page 112), the Fiatagri models were called the G Series and were exactly the same as the Ford machines, being made in the same Canadian factory, but were painted in Fiatagri's terracotta livery. The model numbers are linked to the tractor's power; hence this G190 is powered by a 190hp six cylinder engine. It was after the launch of these tractors that the Fiatagri and Ford names were linked together under the trading name of New Holland.*

The Case International Magnum range were updated in ▶
1995, and the 7100 Series became the 7200 with the 182hp 7120
changing to the 188hp 7220, which is shown here. The rest of the
Magnums remained at the same horsepower, with only their model
numbers changing, although a new flagship model was introduced.
To the right is a bit of a different view of a 7220 showing the
massive rear hydraulics, with a maximum lifting capacity of
7462kg, and the rear extension to the top of the cab that houses the
cab's air filters. By 1996 the 7220's horsepower had risen again,
this time to 200hp.

Another back view, this time of the smallest model in the New ▶
Holland Ford 70 Series range, the 170hp 8670. This tractor's rear
linkage can lift a maximum of 7089kg.

▲ *The Lamborghini 775F Plus is powered by a 75hp three cylinder engine driving through a 12 × 12 transmission. Its price in 1996 was £22,500; compare this with the 92hp Lamborghini 955DT on page 28! This example is shown operating a WestMac bale wrapper. A smaller version is also available, the 60hp 660F Plus.*

◄ *A 260hp engine resides under the bonnet of this John Deere 8400 as it effortlessly pulls a ten furrow Grégoire Besson plough. These two pictures clearly show the extent of glass in the Command View cab, which allows extremely good all-round visibility. Inside the cab, all the main controls are mounted on the CommandARM armrest console that moves with the seat. The powershift transmission, operated by a single lever, gives 16 Y 5 gears and a top speed of 24 mph. The 8400 and 8300 can lift nearly 10t on the rear linkage and a front linkage can also be specified.*

The 130hp six cylinder 6900 came in as the biggest ► *model in the John Deere 6000 range, replacing the smallest of the 7000 Series machines, the 7600. Although of the same design as the other 6000 models, the 6900 features a stronger front axle and extra pto clutches to cope with its extra power.*

▲ *This is the new flagship of the Case International Magnum range, the 264hp six cylinder turbocharged 7250, here seen with an eight furrow Dowdeswell plough. The huge 8.3 litre engines fitted to the Magnum range were developed by Case in conjunction with Cummins and can be run on oilseed rape fuel as well as ordinary diesel, as can many other modern tractors. The Silent Guardian II cab is fitted with heating, cooling and air circulation systems to provide the operator with a perfect working environment and, with large expanses of glass, allows a wide view all around the tractor. By 1996 the 7250's power had been increased to 267hp.*

▲ *New in 1996 is this 70hp four cylinder Same Dorado 70. It is fitted with a 30 X 15 gearbox as standard with a powershift 45 X 45 transmission available as an option. Its smaller sister is the 60hp three cylinder Dorado 60, while the equivalent Lamborghini models are the Sprint 664-60 and 674-70, which replace the earlier 600 and 700 models.*

◄▲ *In the autumn of 1994, the first production versions of Fendt's new system tractors appeared. Prototypes of the Xylon were first seen in 1992 and the final version was available in three models: the 520 (105hp), 522 (125hp) and the 524 (140hp). All are powered by four cylinder MAN water cooled turbocharged engines driving through 44 X 44 Turboshift gearboxes. Sharing several components with the 500 and 800 Series tractors, the Xylon does not look at all like conventional machines, with space for mounted equipment both behind and in front of the centrally mounted cab, as well as a fitted front linkage and a 50 kph road speed.*

◄ *The Massey Ferguson 3000, 3100 and 3600 Series tractors were in production from 1986, but this all came to an end in February 1995 with the new 6100 and 8100 ranges. This 95hp four cylinder 6150 replaced the 3075 and is seen here with a Kverneland power harrow. Although the 6100 Series tractors featured a new cab and styling, they were still basically the same as their predecessors with a choice of Autotronic or Datatronic options. Dynashift was now available throughout the range, however.*

▲ *Inside the cab of this six cylinder Massey Ferguson 6170 of 110hp things are very different from the earlier series. The right hand side control console has been completely revised. The tractor's dashboard also shows more information than that displayed on the previous models and includes a digital forward speed and pto speed indicator. The 6100 range spanned models from the 80hp 6120 up to the top-of-the-range 120hp 6180.*

▲ *Out of Fiatagri's range of five orchard, or narrow, tractors, the 82-86 is the largest with an 80hp four cylinder water cooled engine. Its synchromesh gearbox gives a basic pattern of 12 X 4 gears and a creeper option raises this to 20 X 12. It is available with or without a cab.*

▼ *Various companies have based their products on Ford tractors ever since the Fordson Model F made its appearance back in 1917. Cotil cranes have been made for many years by Colchester Tractors and in the past have been built on Ford 5000 and County chassis. This 1995 Cotil is based on a six cylinder tractor from the Ford New Holland 40 Series range.*

▲ *After taking a major share in Ford New Holland in 1991, it was not long before Fiat became the main shareholder and when this happened changes occurred. With the merger of Ford New Holland and Fiatagri, it was agreed that the new company, New Holland, could use the Ford name for up to ten years and the Ford oval logo for four. As can be seen by this frontal shot of a Ford 7740, the Ford oval had disappeared by 1995 and the Fiatagri leaf emblem took its place, albeit blue instead of brown. This is now the New Holland logo and the same blue leaf appears on all the company's products. At the same time, the 40 Series received a blue roof instead of the previous white, thereby matching the colour scheme of the bigger 70 Series models.*

▲ Two 115hp four cylinder Valmet 6800 tractors, one in yellow and one in red. The Sisu badge that can be seen on the close-up of the bonnet belongs to Valmet's parent company, Sisu Machinery Ltd. ▼

▲ *The Fendt Favorit 511C joined the rest of the German firm's 500 Series tractor line-up in late 1994, the range spanning a total of five models from 95 to 140hp. Equipped with a 115hp six cylinder water cooled engine, the 511C also features a 44 X 44 Turboshift powershift transmission with a top speed of 31 mph as well as Fendt's hydropneumatic front axle suspension system.*

133

▲ *Another New Holland Ford tractor sports the new livery, this time the 85hp four cylinder 6640 drilling with a Nordsten drill and front mounted press.*

▲ *The new Massey Ferguson 8100 range replaced the 3600 Series tractors with six models from 135 to 200hp. This is the 145hp 8120 which, like the rest of the range, came with a side mounted exhaust stack and the Datatronic II system as standard. This new improved Datatronic unit is still mounted inside the cab on the side pillar, but it is larger than the original and has two digital displays, twenty functions, pre-programmable memory and a hard-copy print-out ability;* *it is operated by means of touch pad buttons. The 8110 (135hp), 8120 and the 155hp 8130 are all powered by six cylinder Perkins diesel engines. In April 1994 Massey Ferguson was taken over by the North American AGCO organisation, which already owned the White tractor company and had initially been formed by a buy-out of Deutz-Allis in 1990. The 8120 is shown with a Maschio power harrow and Sulky drill combination.*

▲ *The beginning of 1994 saw the announcement of a joint venture between tractor makers Renault and John Deere. Part of the deal was that Renault would make John Deere 3000 Series tractors in France while the same basic tractor would also appear in the Renault range with Deere engines. The Renault range was called the Ceres Generation II and spanned four models from 55 to 85hp,* *all with four cylinder engines except for the 55hp model which is fitted with a three cylinder unit. The Ceres Series features many more options than its sister John Deere range with an actual total of nine models based on the basic four. Shown here is the 85hp Ceres 95X Tracfor version with a four furrow slatted mouldboard plough.*

▲ *Built in Czechoslovakia since 1946, the Zetor tractor range has been sold in Britain since 1966. This 105hp four cylinder 10540 is fitted with an 18 X 6 gearbox and is shown with a cultivator. Recently Zetor has also made tractors for John Deere to be sold in certain countries.*

◀ *The 'new look' Belarus range of tractors appeared in 1995. This is the 90hp four cylinder 900 model from this large Russian manufacturer, and it is fitted with a 14 X 4 transmission. By 1996 the firm was offering probably its largest ever range of tractors in the UK, ranging from 30 to 350hp wheeled models as well as a range of crawlers spanning 91 to 175hp.*

Seen here powering a Pottinger forager harvester ▶ is the largest in the German Deutz-Fahr tractor line-up. The Agrostar 6.81 produces 190hp from its six cylinder engine and is fitted with a full powershift 18 X 18 gearbox. This tractor is assembled in Italy by Same-Lamborghini-Hürlimann and the rear linkage is capable of lifting an impressive 10,000kg.

◀ *Tractor maker Ursus from Poland imports a range of tractors into Britain including this 47hp three cylinder 3512 and 86hp four cylinder 4514. These tractors bear an uncanny resemblance to the Massey Ferguson 500 and 200 Series ranges. It seems that MF models never die: they just get reincarnated!*

▲ *This Massey Ferguson 8160 ploughing with a Kverneland six furrow plough is fitted with the Dynashift 32 X 32 transmission. The 8160 is now the flagship of the Beauvais built range of tractors with its 200hp six cylinder turbocharged Valmet engine. The 160hp 8140 and 180hp 8150 are also fitted with Valmet power plants. To compete with the other major manufacturers' models of well over 200hp, Massey Ferguson have now begun importing a 240hp Cummins powered tractor from the American White range.*

This 87hp four cylinder Valmet 865 is the biggest model in the ▶
Finnish firm's 65 Series line-up and, unlike the rest of the range which is
fitted with 8 × 4 transmissions, the 865 has a 12 × 8 gearbox.

◀ The 103hp four cylinder
Lamborghini Premium 1050 is part
of the four model 85 to 105hp
Premium range, the biggest of which
is the six cylinder 1060. The
standard 15 × 15 gearbox can be
increased to 60 × 60 and the tractor's
top speed is 40 kph.   142

As is usual with the Same-Lamborghini-Hürlimann group, ▶
when the Lamborghini Premium range was launched, so too were
the accompanying Same and Hürlimann ranges. The Same models
were called Silver and, as with the Lamborghini tractors, comprised
four models but this time from 80 to 100hp. Shown is the 90hp four
cylinder Silver 90, which is fitted with the multi-functional
Pro-active arm attached to the driving seat and housing all the
major controls. The similar Hürlimann range is now imported into
Britain by Zetor importer Motokov UK and is called the XT Series,
with tractors closely following the Premium range of 85 to 105hp
models. The Hürlimann 115 to 135hp Elite and larger Master
ranges are also now available after an absence from the British
market of several years.

Although garden and horticultural tractors are really outside the ▶
scope of this book, it seems only appropriate to mention one of the
largest Japanese tractor makers. Kubota makes a range of tractors
from 34 to 54hp and this is the 37hp 3600 which is powered by a
four cylinder engine and fitted with a 16 X 16 transmission. The
biggest in the range, the 54hp L5450 is unusual in featuring a five
cylinder engine. Another large manufacturer of smaller tractors is
Iseki, who now sell some of the Massey Ferguson 300 Series tractors
in their own livery. This is an ironic turnabout, as for many years
all the main tractor manufacturers have bought in small Japanese
tractors to complement their own ranges.

▲ ▶ *Launched in 1995 the Massey Ferguson 9240 is powered by a six cylinder 240hp Cummins turbo-charged engine. This tractor is actually sourced from the American White tractor range owned by Massey Ferguson's parent company AGCO. With a full powershift 18 x 9 gearbox, the 9240 features components made in Yorkshire by David Brown, the firm that built the first Ferguson tractors back in 1936.*

▲ ▶Ford New Holland bought the Versatile tractor company in 1989 chiefly because Case International had acquired Steiger in 1986 and thus deprived Ford of its supply of the FW Series of high horsepower, articulated, pivot steer, prairie busting tractors. Originally the 325hp Versatile 946 Cummins six cylinder powered tractor was the only model to be imported into Britain, despite several models being sold in North America and Canada, including the earth-shattering 525hp of the biggest of the lot, the 1156. After the merger of Ford New Holland and Fiatagri, the models were revamped with a completely new design of cab and styling; the 80 Series had arrived. This range of articulated leviathans span from 250 to 400hp and are built in the same Winnipeg factory as the 70 and G Series tractors. Shown is the 350hp Cummins powered Ford Versatile 9680 which replaced the 946 as the only model from the 80 Series to be imported into Europe so far. The only way to really appreciate the size of this monster is to stand next to it and look up!

◀ ▶ All the Case International tractor ranges received a new decal design in 1995, with the word 'International' being dropped in favour of the International Harvester initials, so that the Case name is now the most prominent. This is the 100hp six cylinder Maxxum 5130, and inside the cab (right) the gear levers and other controls can be clearly seen. This particular tractor is fitted out to full specification with an air suspension seat, full air conditioning, radio cassette and sun roof. Of course, today this level of comfort is something that most tractor drivers take for granted.

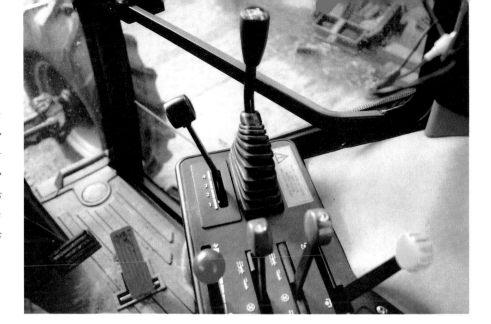

The Mercedes-Benz Unimog concept continues its development with ▶ new machines such as this compact U130 painted in the orange livery used for the non-agricultural market Unimogs.

Smallest in Case International's tractor range and now the only model in the 3200 Series is the 52hp three cylinder 3220, which is only available with the company's LP cab. Two or four wheel drive versions are available and a 8 X 4 transmission is fitted. This example is fitted with grassland tyres and front fenders.

Made by Renault, this is the SE version of the John Deere 3400. Powered by an 85hp four cylinder Deere engine, it is fitted with a 20 X 20 gearbox and is the biggest of the four models in the 3000 range.

◀ ▲ *Introduced in 1995 because of increasing demand for a smaller version of the by then very successful JCB Fastrac, the 1115 has a six cylinder 115hp Perkins diesel engine under its bonnet. It has four equal size wheels, a spacious cab and a load platform at the rear, as well as all round disc brakes. Although sprung, the 1115 does not feature such sophisticated air suspension and braking systems as its bigger brothers because of its smaller size and the need to keep the price down. Therefore, overall speed has been lowered, but despite this it is still faster than conventional tractors.*

▲ *The largest, and the only six cylinder powered, tractor in the Same Silver range is this 100hp 100.6 shown with a WestMac JF mower conditioner.*

▲ *The latest addition to the John Deere stable is this 105hp six cylinder 6506. It slots into the range between the 100hp four cylinder 6400 and the 110hp six cylinder 6600.*

The autumn of 1995 saw Deutz-Fahr introduce an entirely new ▶ range of tractors complete with styling for the next century. After pioneering the droop-nosed tractor in the early 1990s, the new Agrotron models take streamlining to its limits with a short curved bonnet and almost completely glass cab with narrow rounded pillars. This is the 95hp four cylinder 4.95 Agrotron which is fitted with a 24 × 8 powershift transmission.

◀ Another advocate of the sloping bonnet trend is the Austrian tractor maker Steyr. Shown here is just one of three versions available of the 94hp four cylinder 9094. The Steyr range spans models from the 68hp 968 up to the monster 320hp 9320.

The Italian built Hürlimann tractor range includes this 135hp six cylinder Elite H-6135, which is the equivalent of the Same Antares and Lamborghini Formula machines. ▶

◀ The New Holland 40 Series received another face-lift for 1996 with several improvements including extra hydraulic lift capacity and new rubber mudguard extensions, as well as a revised livery. This is the 100hp six cylinder 7840 shown with a Lawrence Edwards bale wrapper wrapping large square bales.

▲ Early 1996 saw New Holland launch two all-new tractor ranges in both Ford and Fiatagri colours. The smaller of the two ranges was the L Series, of which the 85hp four cylinder L85 forms a part. The L Series, built in Modena, Italy, spans four models from 65 to 95hp and are fitted with Iveco diesel engines, new low profile cab and a sloping bonnet.

156

▼ *The Moffett Multi Function Tractor combines agricultural tractor and loading shovel in one machine. Four and six cylinder models are available based on New Holland 40 Series base units. The photographs of the 95hp four cylinder 7740 machine clearly show the redesigned cab to allow for front and back driving positions as well as the rear mounted loader. The tractor's rear linkage, pto, etc are retained so that the MFT can still be used as a conventional farm tractor.* ▼

▲ *Equipped with front and rear mounted Vicon mowers, the 135hp six cylinder turbocharged JCB 1135 is based on the smaller 1115 and is the latest machine to join the Fastrac range, bringing the total number of Fastrac models available to eight, spanning 115 to 170hp.*

▲ *The flagship of the Deutz-Fahr Agrotron range is the 145hp six cylinder 6.45 which is fitted with a 24 x 24 powershift transmission and a rear hydraulic lift capacity of 9240kg. The Agrotron range appeared shortly after the Deutz-Fahr company was taken over by the Italian SLH group, which now trades as Same-Deutz-Fahr.*

Two models from the current Lamborghini line-up. The smallest of the Premium range, the 85hp four cylinder 850, is on the trailer, while the largest machine from this Italian manufacturer, the 189hp six cylinder turbocharged and intercooled 190 Racing, powers a large JF forage harvester.

The Ford 35 Series are the first Italian built Ford tractors, being the same machines as the Fiatagri L models but in Ford colours. As can be seen, the name New Holland now appears on both Ford and Fiatagri tractors, these brand names being given less prominence.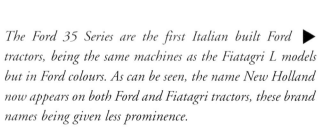

160

The new Mega 50 range was introduced in 1996 by Valmet. This is the ▶ 125hp six cylinder 8150 shown here in white livery. The Valmet Permatorque diesel engines are fitted with a new rotary fuel injection pump, while a 36 X 36 Delta Power Shift transmission and Autocontrol console are also included.

◀ With the 50,000th Case International Maxxum rolling off the production line in 1996, the company have produced special limited edition tractors featuring a chrome exhaust pipe and some rather artistic decals!

▲ *The largest Valmet is now the 8750. This tractor is unique in that its computer controlled Sigma Power system allows the 160hp six cylinder engine to produce up to 190hp at the power take off shaft when required.*

▲ *The New Holland Ford 60 range, along with the identical Fiatagri M models, was launched at the same time as the smaller 35 and L machines in February 1996. This top-of-the-range 160hp six cylinder New Holland 8560 is* *fitted with an 18 X 6 powershift transmission and full electronic control systems. It is shown powering a Kverneland forage harvester, and its sleek styling typifies the modern agricultural tractor of the mid 1990s.*

As the 135hp Massey Ferguson 3635 to the right ▶ ploughs off into the sunset, our look at some of the tractor models of the last thirty years comes to an end. But the development of the agricultural tractor does not. The modern tractor continues to evolve, as it is constantly modified and updated, and during the next thirty years the high-tech computerised tractors of today will probably appear as old-fashioned as the Massey Ferguson 135 or Ford 4000 does now.

INDEX

BOOKS

Ferguson Implements and Accessories   *John Farnworth*
Over 370 illustrations of equipment marketed under the Ferguson Badge starting with the Ferguson Brown and ending with the Massey-Harris-Ferguson.

Tractors at Work   *Stuart Gibbard*
Vols I & II
Each book contains some 180 photographs spanning 1904 to the present and showing a wide range of tractors in many working situations on farms in Britain.

Tractors Since 1889   *Michael Williams*
An overview of the main developments in farm tractors from their stationary steam engine origins to the potential for satellite navigation.

Ford Tractor Conversions: the story
of Doe, Chaseside, Northrop, Muir-Hill,
Matbro and Bray   *Stuart Gibbard*
Detailed, profusely illustrated account of the main models and machines produced by these leading companies.

VIDEOS

Classic Farm Machinery   *Brian Bell*
Vol I 1940-70
Vol II 1970-95
Archive film extracts tracing the mechanisation of the chief arable operations.

Classic Tractors   *Brian Bell*
Archive film extracts focusing on the development of tractors from 1945 to the present.

Henry Ford's Tractors 1907-56   *Michael Williams*
Fordson, the Story of a Tractor
The Massey-Ferguson Tractor Story
John Deere Two-Cylinder Tractors
   (Volumes 1 & 2)
Videos showing in detail the machines produced by these leading companies.